TRUMPETS IN THE MORNING

For Children

LISTEN CHILDREN!
STORY-TIME AGAIN
WHAT TIME IS IT?
OVER THE HILLS AND HOME AGAIN
THE ARK AT THE END OF THE GARDEN
HOBSON'S CHOICE—*For Boys*

For Grown-ups

IF I OPEN MY DOOR
THROUGH OPEN WINDOWS
WHEN WE TWO WALKED
THE WINDS BLOW
A THOUSAND SUNRISES
WHILE THE CANDLE BURNS—*Devotions*
THE LARK IS IN THE SKY
SAFETY LAST—*Tales of the Pacific*
PRODIGAL OF THE SEVEN SEAS—*Biography*
TODAY—*A Book of Devotions*
THERE'S NO PLACE LIKE HOME
AS THE SUN CLIMBS—*Autobiography*
TREES UNAFRAID—(*Lutterworth Press*)
SUNG IN OUR HEARTS—*Studies in the Psalms*
I TURN TO DUCKS
HERE BE PEOPLE
HIS INTERPRETERS
FROM A HILLTOP
SEVEN DAYS OF THE WEEK
THE LADIES OF WESLEYDALE—*Missionary*
I BELIEVE IN THE DAWN
PARTS OF HIS WAYS—*Devotions*
THE KINDLED FLAME

Trumpets in the Morning

STORIES FOR BOYS AND GIRLS

by

RITA F. SNOWDEN

The one thing we need to learn, if life is to be glorious and Christ-like, is the sound of the trumpets in the morning calling us to let the hero within us get the better of the coward.—*Dick Sheppard, in an address to boys and girls.*

LONDON

THE EPWORTH PRESS

FIRST PUBLISHED IN 1960

© THE EPWORTH PRESS 1960

Book Steward:
FRANK H. CUMBERS

SET IN MONOTYPE BASKERVILLE AND PRINTED IN
GREAT BRITAIN BY THE CAMELOT PRESS LTD
LONDON AND SOUTHAMPTON

AUTHOR'S NOTE

A FEW of these stories made their first appearance in the *Expository Times*, and I am grateful to the Editor for his ready agreement to their being reprinted here. I must also acknowledge a debt to Author and Publisher for the use I have made of a conversation in *Africa Drums*, by Richard St Barbe Baker (George Ronald, Oxford).

R. F. S.

CONTENTS

THE LITTLE BOY WITH THE BIG BAT

EVERYBODY in Len's home loved cricket. Mrs Hutton pretended she didn't on the occasions she heard the sudden crash of a ball through her window; but that didn't happen often.

Len was only a little fellow of nine when his father took him and his brothers and other boys of Pudsey out on to the green, for 'a bit of practice'. Mrs Hutton could never hold them back long enough to eat a decent tea, they were so keen. Again and again, they scrambled through tea, and made off. The hours till dusk were all too short for the young enthusiasts. There was so much to learn if they were to be good cricketers.

Usually there were six of them—not enough to divide into sides—so each had a turn with the bat, and stayed in till the others got him out, however long it took.

Once Len, then so small that the bat-handle stuck into his middle, stayed in all Monday evening, all Tuesday, and Wednesday and Thursday, and was still at the bat when they broke up on Friday. Never did his playmates allow him to forget it; nor did he forget it himself. It was a kind of foretaste of 1938—in the unguessed future— when he would bat for two and a half days at the Oval, and set up the record Test score of 364 against Australia. But little Len, at nine years of age, was still learning to manage his bat.

Boyhood was full of long summer evenings, when as dusk gave way to dark, his father called across the green: 'Come on, Len . . . home to bed!'

'Nay,' he would call back, 'give us a bit longer!'

'You've had enough,' his father would call.

But Len could never have enough of cricket. The most exciting sound in the whole world to him was the sound of the ball on the bat. Every spare moment between lessons and work, he filled with cricket—practising new skills. With much effort, he saved up to buy a splendid bat—of a size that wouldn't stick into his middle.

'He'll be the best cricketer of us all in the end,' said his father, as he saw how keen he was, and how practice was improving his game. He was right. Len, grown up, was the best cricketer of them all, and no one was more proud of him than his family and friends of Pudsey, who had played with him between tea and the coming of dusk.

Every moment of his grown-up cricket days Len enjoyed as much—trying always in England, or in Australia, among many fine cricketers, to do everything he could to further the game.

There were many unforgettable matches during those years, but the greatest moment of all was when Len was chosen Captain of all England. So well did he captain his team that not once in the four glorious years of his captaincy did he lose a series. Our Queen made him a knight of her realm, so that now he is called *Sir* Leonard Hutton.

But when Len came to look back, and to tell his story in two fine books, *Cricket is My Life* and *Just My Story*, it was not *only* of his family's encouragement with the bat and ball that he thought gladly. 'When I was a boy,' he said, 'I was made to go to Sunday School and church every week. Like most boys, I was not particularly keen about doing so at the time, *but I have been grateful since to my parents for putting me on the right path.*'

SUGAR FOR THE HORSE

SOMETIMES when I open my big London newspaper, *The Times*, it seems too big. It is so full of big and important news that to read it all would take all day, and I should get no work done at all. Then it would be next morning—and there would be another copy of *The Times* waiting. So big and important is this famous London paper, so full of people and happenings—weddings and wars, and rich people's deaths, and pictures and plays, and travellers in far distant lands!

But this morning, as I was looking through *The Times*, I came across an exciting piece of news, right at the top of a column, that wasn't about a big and important person, or a rich person, or a traveller in a far distant land, but about a little boy and a horse.

It happened on Michael's first visit to London one icy winter's day. Michael—whose other name is Bartlett—lives in a place called Wallington, in Surrey, and on this visit to the great city with his father and mother, he happened to see a policeman's horse named Dante slip and fall outside his stable in Great Scotland Yard. Though Dante managed to struggle up again on to his feet without unseating his rider, it was a nasty thing to happen.

Though Michael and his father and mother moved away, and the day was crammed with other sights, he couldn't get Dante out of his mind. At night, when he was safely tucked up in bed, he couldn't help wondering how Dante was feeling, and if he was hurt. He talked about him so much that in the end his father promised to write a letter to New Scotland Yard, where the London policemen have their offices, and ask about Dante.

When the letter was written, Michael added to it a small box from his toy cupboard, full of sugar-lumps 'to make the horse better', and a bar of chocolate 'for the kind rider'.

Now a very official-looking letter has come for Michael from a senior Metropolitan police official, telling him about Dante, and thanking him for his concern.

It was such a surprising thing for such a very little boy to get such a big and important-looking letter, that somebody told *The Times* Editor. And although he had lots of news waiting to go into his paper—news of weddings and wars, and deaths of rich people, and pictures and plays, and travellers in far distant lands—he put this piece of news about Michael into the very top of a column in his paper. He plainly hoped that lots of people would read it—and I, for one, did. And that just shows how wise that Editor is—*for any little thing that is kind is really big and important*, and deserves a place in the newspaper.

Some of the loveliest words of Jesus—part of His Sermon on the Mount—are called the Beatitudes (Matthew 5[1-12]). Each one begins with the word 'Blessed'—'*Blessed* are the merciful: for they shall obtain mercy. *Blessed* are the pure in heart: for they shall see God.' They are a little hard for small boys and girls, so somebody has made some Children's Beatitudes—easy to understand. 'Blessed' means 'Happy', and each one begins with 'Happy'. The very first one says:

'*Happy are they who are kind to dumb creatures*, for they are the children of the Father who made all things.

'Happy are they who laugh when they feel like crying, for they shall be called God's heroes.

'Happy are they who forgive others quickly, for God's sunshine shall be upon their faces.

'Happy are they who want very much to grow up wise and good, for God is their helper.'

THE LITTLE SHIPS

THE sun was on the blue sea and the gulls wheeled over-
head as we left for the little Dutch island of Marken. For
a long time the fisher-folk have lived there, but one day
soon, when the big task of draining the water away from
the land is finished, it won't be an island any longer.
Then it will be possible to visit Marken by land, and the
ship that took us there will have other work to do.

Over the blue-painted jetty and rails the fishing-nets
hang. The air is sweet and salty, and at any time you
may see an old fisherman in his black wooden clogs and
his baggy blue breeches, enjoying the sight. All his life
he has worn the same kind of clothes, and all his life he
has loved the sea. He has sailed out into the fishing
grounds of the Zuyder Zee when it has been blue and
calm, and when angry storms have beaten up to endanger
the ships. But now he does not go far from the village,
where the pointed houses along the jetty-side are painted
bright green, blue or yellow.

At the end of the village, in an open space, where lots
of narrow ways meet, is the church. For a long time now,
the old fisherman in the black wooden clogs and the big
blue breeches has been taking care of it. He is not the
minister—'the Dominee' as they call him in Marken—he
does not preach and teach. He looks after the church—
opening it up in the morning, closing it safely at night,
and keeping it clean and tidy for the services when the
people from all over Marken come to worship. He is
very happy to be able to do this, for he loves his church
even more than he loves the sea—and that is a very
great deal. His name is Jan Peereboom, and when he
is not in the church, he is busy tidying up his own little
house.

It was late afternoon when we knocked at his door. The

preacher's little girl had come with us from her own house, to make sure that we found the way. When he heard our knock, old Jan came and opened the door. He was busy getting his meal, but when we told him we had come a long way to see the church he came at once with the big key. All the way there as we walked together, his wooden clogs making pleasant noises on the cobbles, he told us the story of the church, going back for four hundred years.

Once inside, there was lots to see. The thing that old Jan was most proud of was the thing that met our eyes first, the neat models of ships hanging up in the roof of the church. Big ones and little ones, they hung just above the heads of the worshippers, where they could be seen all the time. And each one, correct in every detail, had been made with the utmost love and skill.

The first one, a lugger, was about twenty-four inches in length, gay with pennant and sail and complete with fishing-net. The next was a sailing-ship, for catching eels. The third was a herring-boat—a *buis*—one of the oldest boats of all. As we admired it, old Jan went into the vestry and brought out a picture of a fleet of *buis* sailing out from Marken. 'Now there is only one left,' said he. 'And is this the kind of boat you fished from?' we asked him. 'Yes,' he said. 'For thirty-five fishing seasons I went out into the great seas in a boat like that.' And his eyes shone as he remembered it—all the hazards of sunshine and storm.

'But why have the fishermen hung the little boats in the church?' we asked.

'Ah,' said old Jan. 'That is because we have come back safely; and we like to remember that every task we do we offer to God's glory. For us it is fishing the great seas— and we like to remember that He accepts our offering when we bring it with humility and love.'

We have no little model ships hanging in the roofs of

our churches, because we are not fishermen; we have other work to do. But we have a verse in the New Testament which should be a good reminder to us that every task we do is important. It says: '*Whatsoever ye do, do all to the glory of God!*' (1 Corinthians 10[31]).

THE NAUGHTY ELEPHANTS

ONCE there was a boy in Cornwall who loved animals. His first animal friend was a donkey. He loved his donkey, and though it wandered away on to the moors, he always knew where to find it and how to get it back.

In time he grew up, and when the war came he became a soldier in the Camel Corps. So his next animal friend was a camel. Next, he was made a transport-officer in charge of mules and anyone could see he was good with animals.

But his best adventure of all was after the war, in Burma. In that hot, jungle country he got a job with elephants. In Burma, elephants are used to drag teak logs out of the jungle. Teak is one of the world's best hardwoods, and the great trees grow so high up on the mountain sides that only elephants can be used to drag the logs down and out of the jungle. But the elephants enjoy their work, and with their trunks build the logs into rafts, so that they can be floated down the rivers to Mandalay or Rangoon.

It is hard work, and the jungle is very hot, so the elephants need plenty of rests. They have Burmese boys, 'oozies', to sit on their necks and drive them, but they need good white masters to take care of them, too, and that was the job of the young Cornishman who by now went by the nickname 'Elephant Bill'.

He loved his elephants just as he'd loved the other animals and tried in every way to take care of them. It didn't take the elephants long to know that they had a good master. Some of them were old and wise, and they knew at once; but some were young and had been born in the jungle camp, and had never known any other life. They were happy young elephants, smashing through the jungle looking for nice, green things to eat, or bathing in the warm water-holes, splashing each other like noisy boys at play. Sometimes, when the big elephants came in too, the 'oozie' would scrub them all over with a piece of creeper that lathered up like soap. They loved that.

But there were useful things for young elephants to learn. It didn't take them long when 'Elephant Bill' and his boys harnessed them. With wooden panniers on their backs and strong ropes twisted from the bark of jungle trees, they were able to help. That was a proud moment. Sometimes—rather like boys—when work was over, and they were let out, they got up to tricks. But 'Elephant Bill' loved his elephants—though he found them out again and again.

Every elephant was given a bell round its neck, so that when it wandered off to look for juicy green leaves, it could be found again. The tinkle of the bells, each one with a slightly different note, told where the elephants were. The old, wise working elephants liked that. But some of the naughty young elephants would plug up the little bells that hung round their necks with thick stodgy mud, so that the clappers couldn't ring. Then they would steal into a grove of cultivated bananas at night.

But when morning came, there was trouble for everybody. Always the light revealed the damaged grove—the fruit eaten, the young leaves broken down. 'Elephant Bill' was in trouble, the 'oozies' were in trouble, and the naughty young elephants were in trouble—all because they had cunningly defeated the good use of their bells.

Boys and girls are just a little like elephants. God hasn't given us each a bell to hang round our necks, but He has given us something more wonderful—a conscience. It is like a bell *within* us, helping us to do the right instead of the wrong. When we do wrong things, it tells us quite clearly—unless, like the naughty young elephants, we silence it. That leads to trouble for everybody. Our conscience, like the bell, is to help us. As St Paul told his young friend Timothy in a letter now in our New Testament, 'A *pure heart* and a *good conscience*' go together.

RINGING THE BELLS

Do you like climbing into high, scrambly places? It's fun, though you get the shivers when you look down. There are lots of places like that, and one of them is Winchester Cathedral in the south of England.

The Cathedral is very old, very beautiful, and very high. For a thousand years boys and girls have worshipped in Winchester. At first, it was only a little church, but the people loved it and worshipped God in it. Then, sad to say, it was destroyed. But the people who lived in Winchester then knew that they couldn't manage without a church, so they built another—a bigger one. In time, sad to say, that also was destroyed.

But the people in Winchester of that day too set to work with all their might to build another. It rose so beautiful and so big, that they called it a Cathedral, and many people flock to it today.

A little while ago, a friendly man named H. V. Morton went to Winchester and spent an interesting hour inside the Cathedral. There was no service on at the time, so the verger came forward, gathered a little group about him, and surprised them by asking, 'Who's coming up to the roof with me?'

All in that little group—boys and girls, 'solemn elderly women, fat men, thin men', looked at him for a moment in surprise but soon they were starting up the spiral staircase—up and up, round and round, puffing and puffing, round and round. Every time they paused for a breath, the kindly verger told them some more of the wonderful story of the Cathedral.

Of course, none of them dreamed it would be so far, as round and round they went, holding on tight to the hand-ropes, feeling the smooth face of the stone in the dark.

But at last they got to the top—right up over the highest part of the Cathedral, where far below were the seats for the people who gathered to worship. Above their heads were great oaken beams that the Normans had felled eight hundred years before.

But the greatest interest was the bells. The members of that little group had all heard them down below, and now they were surprised to be so near. Soon, the verger gathered them all in close—boys and girls, 'solemn elderly women, fat men, thin men', puffing a good deal, and gave them a little lecture on bell-ringing.

They didn't know anything about bell-ringing, but presently he numbered them off from left to right. Each, according to his number, then became responsible for one bell. Only the verger knew what he would do next. But as he called a number—turning quickly from one to another—each, because he was told, played. To everyone's surprise, from that odd little group away up in the bell-tower of Winchester Cathedral came forth the hymn-tune, 'Abide with me'.

It was not possible, of course, for any of them to know how it sounded down on the ground. Only one thing was certain: it couldn't have sounded as good as when the *real* bell-ringers played it—*for there's all the difference in the world in just doing a thing one is told to do, without understanding it, and doing it out of a full heart, with knowledge and joy, for the sheer love of it.*

Jesus knew people whose religion was like that. The Priests told them what to do—and they did it. They just kept the rules. The Priests said that no one was to carry a burden on the Sabbath day—so they wouldn't even light a fire on the Sabbath because the kindling wood would count as a burden. They wouldn't cook a meal—because they would have to carry the burden of a cooking-pot. A tailor was not even allowed to carry his needle, stuck in his coat, because that was a burden, and no man with a wooden leg was allowed to go out on the

Sabbath. A father whose little child cried—was forbidden to pick him up because that meant a burden.

So stupid and meaningless it all became! There was no joy in a religion like that and no warm, eager love. Like the people up in the tower of Winchester, they just did what they were told to do without thinking for themselves at all. It was, of course, a kind of religion—but it wasn't the best kind.

There are some things that we have to do because we are told to do them; but the best things in the world, Jesus said, are those we do out of a good, glad heart, knowing what we are doing.

TEN TIES

In London lately, a lady named Mrs Bannister went to buy ten very special ties all exactly alike.

Mrs Bannister is the wife of Dr Roger Bannister, the four-minute-mile runner, and the ties were for her husband and for nine other members of the most *exclusive* club in the world. So exclusive is this club, that you could only get in if you passed a very important test.

It was no use looking in the shops though they had lots of bright, beautiful ties, with stripes and dots and twirly patterns. She wanted something very special, and she made her way to Regent Street to find Mr Styles—a clever designer of silverware, who was doing work for the Royal Household. It might seem at first a funny thing to go to a designer of silverware for a tie, but Mrs Bannister knew what she was doing.

She talked it over with Mr Styles, and when he got over the surprise of being asked to design a tie, he set to work. He thought of all the fine records of Dr Roger Bannister as an athlete; and he thought of those who, with him, would be allowed to wear the tie, and at last, when he had puzzled it out, he drew several designs for Mrs Bannister to see so that she could have a choice.

At last, out of them all, Mrs Bannister chose a very handsome design. It showed a silver '4' with two 'M's'—representing the two words 'mile' and 'minute'—to be woven round the '4' in gold. Then round that was a laurel wreath in gold. Mrs Bannister was very pleased with it. I think Mr Styles was pleased, too, that he had been able to satisfy his unusual customer.

Then the design had to be taken away from the designer's in Regent Street, woven in silk and made up by a tie-maker.

It took a lot of thought and clever planning and

workmanship to get the ten ties made for the ten athletes who, like Dr Roger Bannister, had achieved a four-minute mile. Only those ten could belong to the 'Four-minute-mile Club'.

Nobody can begrudge them the joy of wearing their exclusive ties, and belonging to the most *exclusive* club in the world—but I am glad you and I can belong to the most *inclusive* company in the world.

It isn't a club, of course. It's the Christian Church. It is by far the biggest thing in the world to which anyone can belong—though we don't have to wear a tie to show how special it is. There is nothing else in the world like it; nobody is too young, and nobody is too old; nobody is too rich, and nobody is too poor. It doesn't matter where you live—in the town or the country; in a big land, or in a little land—a tropical island in the Pacific, or away up in the snowy wastes of Alaska. It doesn't matter whether you have a brown face, or a white one, a yellow one or a black one. It only matters that you want to belong, and that you own Jesus as your Lord and Master in everything that you do. For He is the Head of the Christian Church—and anybody can belong.

Even at the very beginning, there were more than ten— there were twelve: fishermen Peter and James and John, beside the Sea of Galilee, and the others. And now, all over the world, there are more boys and girls, and big people belonging than ever before. It's lovely to think about, isn't it, when we sing our hymn?—

> *Far round the world Thy children sing their song:*
> *From East and West their voices sweetly blend,*
> *Praising the Lord in whom young lives are strong,*
> *Jesus our Guide, our Hero, and our Friend.*

FAR AND NEAR

THE famous artist got the surprise of his life. And no wonder. His servant came to say that there was a lion at the door. Sir Edwin Landseer was having a little doze after lunch, and he must have thought he was dreaming.

'Did you order a lion, sir?' asked the servant.

'A lion?' exclaimed the famous artist.

'Yes, sir. There's a lion at the door in a cab,' answered the servant.

And there was. It had been sent up from the Zoo, a wonderful beast with a great shaggy mane. Of course, it was dead.

When the famous artist got over his shock he was glad to see it. He had it brought into his studio, and for thirty-six hours without stopping he studied it, till he could remember everything about it. He made clever sketches of it, and lots of notes.

A tall column of stone already stood waiting in Trafalgar Square. Sir Edwin Landseer had promised to model four great lions to crouch at the base of it, but he'd never been able to do them.

But today, anybody who goes into Trafalgar Square, London, can see Landseer's lions. In their midst the fine column of stone towers above wide steps, and four carvings of famous battles. One commemorates Trafalgar and the death of Lord Nelson, on his famous *Victory*. This is the Nelson monument, and the figure of Nelson in stone stands on the very top of it.

It is a hundred and eighty-four feet from the ground, so that if you stand and crick your neck and look up, it seems to fade away to a point, because it is so high. Actually, the flat platform just below the figure of Nelson is large enough to have allowed fourteen people to have dinner there before the figure was put up. Nelson's figure itself is seventeen feet two and a half inches—the height of three ordinary men. He was put up in three great pieces, neatly fitted together, the largest piece weighing thirty tons. It must have been a great task getting him up there.

But now he looks so small, and such a long, long way off. The famous column stands out as a landmark, but you can't really see what Nelson himself is like. That is why it was of such great interest when somebody thought of making a model of Nelson's statue and showing it at a recent Exhibition in London so that people could look at him closely.

Londoners who came to the Exhibition were delighted —they had always wondered what Nelson was really like; *and now they knew.*

It was something like that that the people of Palestine felt when Jesus came among them. Nothing like it had ever happened before. For a long, long time they had known that God had made the world, and done many wonderful things—but they didn't really know much about Him. He was like the figure of Nelson in London, high up above them.

Then God revealed His wonderful plan—and all was changed. This is how our New Testament recorded it: 'God (the Word) was made flesh, and dwelt among us, and we beheld His glory.' When Jesus walked in and out of the homes of the people, telling stories to their little children, healing the sick, close beside them, and they asked Him what God was like, He said: '*God is like Me. He who has seen Me, has seen God the loving Father.*'

That made all the difference in the world—and it still does. We, too, can now know what God is like—not far away, remote in the heavens, but close beside us, in Jesus, helping us and loving us all the time.

UP THE CHESTNUT TREE

THE wheels of the train sang a happy song—taking me to the home of my friend, Dr Hugh: 'You'll soon be there; you'll soon be there; you'll soon be there!' And I was.

Soon Dr Hugh was putting my suitcase into the back of his car; soon opening his gate with the little brass plate on it bearing his name in shining letters. Everything within shone with friendship and welcome.

Soon we were sharing a cosy fire, and tea and cake; soon we were sharing talk of the church—for everyone in that happy home loves the church, and the doctor himself leads the junior choir; soon we were sharing books in bright jackets on the bookshelves; and lots of stories—some of them surprising, some of them amusing. One of them I want to share with you.

When Dr Hugh was a boy, he lived in a town called Hamilton, and went to a church called St. Paul's. It was a fine church, and he was the boy who blew the organ. Every Sunday when the organist, Mr Webster, seated himself at the organ ready to play, young Hugh used to seat himself out of sight behind the organ ready to pump the air in.

As well as the people in the church, who joined in the singing, Mr Webster, the organist, and young Hugh, there was the minister. The Reverend William Ready was a famous, much-loved minister, and a great preacher. He preached for three-quarters of an hour, morning and evening. It never seemed a minute too long to anyone except young Hugh, who used sometimes to slip away from his little corner.

One Sunday morning the minister happened to have a very sore throat. He managed to start his sermon, but after he had been preaching about ten minutes he suddenly stopped and said that they would sing the last hymn.

Straightaway, Mr Webster opened his great book at the proper place, and put his fingers to the keys—but no music came. For a moment he couldn't think what was the matter. Then he slipped off his stool, and took a quick look where the organ-blower sat—but there was no organ-blower there! In a panic, Mr Webster then dashed into the vestry—still he could not be found! Then out into the churchyard he dashed, casting an anxious look up a giant chestnut-tree.

In less time than it takes to tell he got young Hugh down out of that tree, and taking hold of him firmly, laid him across his knee, and gave him 'three of the best'. Then together they hurried back into the church.

Think of it! The congregation was there, the minister was there, the organist was there—but the organ-blower had gone up the chestnut-tree!

Dr Hugh and I chuckled heartily as he told it. In the New Testament is a text which he now never forgets. It is Moffatt's translation of 1 Corinthians 3⁹. It says: 'We work together!'

THE BEST SONG OF ALL

ARE you a good singer? Can you sing the low notes and the high notes, and all in between, strongly and sweetly, so that it is a pleasure to hear?

Some boys and girls are such good singers that they are allowed to sing on the wireless. One night in May 1926 a very special singer came over the wireless of the BBC for the very first time. Those who were lucky enough to be listening in at that moment, were thrilled with joy. No, it was not a boy, singing lovely, clear, liquid notes; it was not a girl. It was not even a lady or a gentleman. It was a little brown bird. And as people listened—some of them lonely people far from home, some of them sick people in hospital—the joy and beauty of the song touched their hearts.

At the end of the year, when the BBC asked its listeners which song they had liked best of all that they had heard, they replied *the song of the little brown bird*—the nightingale. It was a song, they said, that reminded them of the lovely, quiet, refreshing green of the woods. It had been all the better for a surprise.

People have always loved the nightingale—and some have made poems about its song. I want to tell you of someone who was lame, and who loved the nightingale especially. He lived in beautiful Italy. His name was Epictetus.

He lived in a great house, but it wasn't his house, for Epictetus, sad to say, was a slave. His master wasn't a very kind master, being hard on his slaves and flattering to his friends. Epictetus had another great trouble—he was lame. But although he was a slave, his thoughts and imagination were free.

When he had not to wait on his master, he would hobble off to where a wonderful teacher taught every day.

Sometimes he taught in the streets. Epictetus loved listening to him. He hardly noticed how cramped his lame legs were as he squatted on a step, or how tired he became with standing when there was nowhere to squat.

At last a day came when Epictetus himself was allowed to teach in the streets. He loved that. But he was stopped; a new Emperor came and many things were changed. The Emperor Domitian would not allow any teaching in the streets, and an order went out that all teachers were to stop, or dreadful things would be done to them.

Because Epictetus, who was now an old man, wanted more than anything to live and teach his beautiful thoughts to others, he fled to a place called Nicopolis. There, where the Emperor had no power over him, he set up again, and was soon so happy in his teaching that he almost forgot he was lame and poor.

He lived in a funny little house that had no door, and no need of a door, for there was nothing within save a few cooking-pots and a straw mattress. But Epictetus didn't feel poor; he felt rich.

One of his pupils wrote down some of the things he said so that they would never be forgotten—and one of these was his saying about the little nightingale whose songs lifted up his heart. '*If I were a nightingale, I would pour out my life in song to Him; but being just an old lame man, what shall I do but praise and bless Him as I am able.*'

Wasn't that a lovely thing to say? Old, lame and poor! God would value his praise. He waits also for youthful praise—the praise of boys and girls.

A LITTLE BOY AND A PUPPY

THE dew had long gone from the grass when the Traveller made his way in through the gates of the little town. The people were about their own affairs, and few walked in the streets.

The Traveller had never been that way before, and no one had told him what might be seen. But he had not gone far when he met a man in fine clothes. 'I believe you are a stranger,' said he. 'I am this town's Chief Citizen.'

'I am honoured to meet you,' said the Traveller. 'Yes, I am a stranger, and I would be glad of your help.'

'You will not find such another town in a month's journeying from dawn till dusk,' said the Chief Citizen. 'And there is one thing you must not miss—the statue at the cross-ways.'

'Thank you,' said the Traveller. 'Your pride in it suggests to me that it is a fine piece of art. I shall not miss it, I assure you.'

'You honour our town in your interest in our statue,' said the Chief Citizen, 'and me especially. Was I not chairman of the committee that put it there? Was it not my word that decided that it should be at the cross-ways?'

With those proud words of the Chief Citizen ringing in his ears, the Traveller passed on.

But he could not find the street that would lead him to the cross-ways and the statue. He tried one street, and then another, and it led him into a lane full of little houses and workshops. Feeling that he would never find his way unhelped, he knocked at a workshop door. The man inside was busy with chisel and mallet. The sound of his tools on the stone he was fashioning reached the Traveller's ears before the door was opened to him. As the Traveller stood in the sunlit doorway, the Mason asked, 'What can I do for you? I see you are a stranger.'

The Traveller replied: 'After I came through the gates of your town, I met the Chief Citizen, who urged me to see the statue at the cross-ways. But it seems I have lost my way. You know the statue, of course, could you show me the way to take?'

'You have come to the right door, I assure you,' said the Mason. 'You couldn't have chosen a better door at which to knock. I, of all men in this town, ought to be able to direct you. Did I not fashion the statue? Chosen of all who applied for the task, I was. And believe me, I never did a finer piece of work. Indeed, there is no finer statue in a dozen towns around.'

And with that proud word, and his directions, the Traveller passed out of the lane where the Mason's workshop stood, to the wide road beyond.

But the wide road did not at once lead him to the cross-ways, as he hoped it would. Fortunately, at a bend, he met a Roadman, chopping off weeds. He looked up from under his wide-brimmed hat, and leaned on his hoe. 'Good day to you!' said he. 'I see you are a stranger. It's shocking how weeds grow—I'm always chopping them off, and they are growing as fast again, the moment my back is turned.'

'You seem to have an unending job,' said the Traveller. 'Can you tell me the road to the cross-ways and the statue?'

'Now, fancy you putting that question to the one man in this town who happens to know,' said the Roadman proudly. 'Don't I keep the weeds chopped in front of the statue in a way that wins everyone's praise? Travellers who come here to the little town always remark upon it—the tidiest roadsides they've seen anywhere in the world, they say. I'm real proud of it, I am.'

And, thinking over the Roadman's pride, the Traveller bade him good-day and went on his way. Surely he would soon be at the cross-ways.

Just as he was wondering how far it could be to the

C

statue, he came upon a boy sitting on the grass of the roadside, playing with a little puppy. Both seemed full of happiness—so simple, so happy that they hadn't time to be proud. The Traveller stopped, and once more put his question about the cross-ways and the statue. 'Do you mean Jesus?' asked the little boy, hugging his puppy, as he rose to answer the Traveller's question. 'Why, you're almost there. Come. I will lead you to Him.'

And as they went on together, the Traveller suddenly realized that none of the others had told him anything about the statue, but only about themselves; the most important thing about them was their pride. As he looked down at the little boy at his side, holding his puppy, something that the One whom he loved above all others had said came into his mind, standing there before His statue, at the cross-ways. And the little boy looked up with surprise to hear him say it: '*Of such is the Kingdom of Heaven!*'

GIFTS FOR THE PALACE

ARE you ready? I want to take you to a beautiful palace. It's a very unusual palace, because no kings or queens or princes or princesses have ever lived in it. It sounds like a once-upon-a-time story, but it's not: it's a right-up-to-the-minute story, for I was there myself lately.

This beautiful and unusual palace is in Holland. It is called The Palace of Peace. All around it—you will see as we enter the great gates—are beautiful grounds. Many gardeners must be employed to keep them, with their flower-beds and trees.

At the door is a clever guide, who speaks four languages —Dutch, French, German, English—but we will pass him by, because I want to take you round myself.

First, I must tell you how this beautiful and unusual palace came to be here at all. About sixty years ago—in 1899—a great peace conference of people from all over the world met in Holland to decide how the nations could live together without war. 'War,' they said, as they talked it over, 'is stupid and cruel and evil. We will have no more war. But in order to build up a peaceful world, we must have a place where we can meet together to discuss our problems.'

It seemed such a fine idea, that they agreed at once to build a palace where they could meet—a Palace of Peace.

'It must be one of the most beautiful buildings we can make,' they said. 'So we'll have a competition, and the architect who sends in the best design shall have the honour of helping.' And it was so. From all over the world designs came in, and the best one was chosen. The builders set to work. They laid the foundations. Then they said, 'We must have this beautiful Palace of Peace made of the very best materials in the world, and everyone must help.' And they did.

The wrought-iron gates, and the bronze doors into the Palace itself were the gift of the German Government, made by the clever craftsmen of that country. They are the first things we see as we come to the Palace, and beautiful they are.

But before we go inside to look at the many gifts there, I must tell you that the granite on which the Palace is built, came from Sweden, and the granite used for the porches came from Norway.

As soon as we step into the Palace, I'm sure the first thing to catch your eye will make you say, 'O-o-o-h! How beautiful!' It is; it's the beautiful bronze and crystal candelabra hanging from the ceiling, ever so high up. That was the gift of the Austrian Government.

Before you now is the wide sweeping staircase of the Palace, leading up to the Court of Justice, and the great Conference room. From there you can see through the windows an enclosed courtyard, with a fountain playing in the middle.

But that must wait a minute; there are so many things to see, with corridors that invite us through the Palace. You must look a moment at a great vase that came from Russia—it stands higher than you do—I'm sure you've never seen such a giant vase. I can't think where else it would fit, except in this Palace. There is another priceless one from China, and there are others as well from Hungary—all gifts.

On the walls you will see more as you look round, and I can hear you say 'O-o-o-h!' again, for here are hung tapestries with pictures worked out in beautiful colours and millions and millions of stitches so small that you can't see them. Besides them are priceless paintings; both tapestries and paintings came from France.

When at last you are ready to climb the wide sweeping staircase, you will see a group of statues, the gift of America, and you will want to stop to look at them a long time. The carpets that you walk on, that make you feel you are walking on air, came from Turkey and Rumania. The Government of Holland itself gave the decorations for the walls here, and also the fountain in the courtyard that you now have time to look at. The modelled polar bears standing at each corner remind us that Denmark sent a gift, too. Belgium, for all that she is a little country, sent doors.

So all the countries had a share. Britain sent the stained-glass windows on the staircase and in the great hall—showing the craftsman's skill in beautiful colours. It really is a most beautiful palace; with everybody helping, it took six years to build. It was ready in the summer of 1913.

It had been open for exactly one year when, in spite of what everybody had said, war broke out. Germany, who had given the handsome gates, suddenly marched into Belgium, who had given the doors. Britain and France, though they had given the stained-glass windows, and the priceless paintings, joined up to fight Germany. Holland itself was soon ravaged and ruined by gun-fire and the march of armies.

What had happened? What about the beautiful Palace of Peace? What about all the promises? Yes, that was just the point. For the truth is that those many nations who had talked so much, and built the beautiful Palace of Peace, spent too little on peace itself.

Jesus said: 'Blessed are the peace-*makers*'; and though they had given their carpets and vases and pictures, that wasn't enough—it takes more than that to make peace. It takes justice, and trust, and help, and friendship, and a great deal of time and energy and thought.

So the beautiful Palace stands today, to remind us all— boys and girls, and grown-ups—of the words of Jesus: 'Blessed are the peace-*makers*: for they shall be called the children of God' (Matthew 5⁹).

HOW THE HORRID CORNER WAS CHANGED INTO THE HAPPY CORNER

ONCE there was a famous artist called Edward Burne-Jones. His head was full of thoughts, and his hands were so clever that with paints and brushes he could make beautiful pictures that people came from near and far to see.

This famous artist had a daughter; and she had a daughter too—a very little daughter. Edward Burne-Jones loved them both, his little grand-daughter especially, and they had lovely times together.

One evening the little girl got into a naughty mood; twice she disobeyed her mother, and her mother had to punish her. She stood sobbing in a corner, a very sad sight. Of course, her wise grandfather couldn't interfere, but he felt sad too. At last the little girl's sobs stopped, and she felt really sorry for what she had done. When she had told her mother and her grandfather that she was sorry, it was time to kiss good-night and go up to bed.

First thing in the morning, when the sun came peeping into her room, she remembered the night before. Slowly she washed and dressed, and quietly she crept downstairs. When she got to the closed door, she waited for some minutes. Then reaching up to the big door-knob, she turned it, and went in. Already her grandfather was there busy with his paints. But she could not bear to look into his face, and she took care not to look into that horrid corner. But when she did look into her grandfather's face, she found a beautiful smile. And that gave her courage to look into the horrid corner. Do you know, something had happened to that, too. It wasn't a bit like it was when she stood sobbing in it—before she had said she was sorry and was forgiven. For that same morning, just to make it plain that she was forgiven, her grandfather had risen specially early, and had painted on to the walls of that horrid corner the happiest things he could think of—angels, little rabbits, birds and butterflies and roses.

Of course, it was the same corner; but in a way, it wasn't at all the same, because as soon as that little girl had said she was sorry, she was forgiven, and that always changes things.

Her mother and her grandfather had learned that, of course, from Jesus. Once Jesus had a grown-up friend who did something wrong—he denied Him beside a fire of coals. His name was Peter. When somebody said that he was a friend of Jesus, he said he wasn't, and that he didn't know Him. But that was only half of his story, too. For after a while, Peter was sorry—and Jesus forgave him beside another fire of coals. So ever afterwards, instead of a fire of glowing coals reminding him of a horrid moment, it reminded him of a happy one.

That is still Jesus' way. A verse in our New Testament says so: 'If we confess our sins, He is faithful and just to forgive us our sins' (1 John 1⁹). That is some of the best news in the world—how horrid corners in our lives can be changed into happy ones!

THE LITTLE PEDLAR

EVERY boy and girl who goes to worship in St Mary's Church, Lambeth, London, loves the little Pedlar. He is such a cheery little fellow. Rain, wind or shine, he is there, going upon his way, his staff in hand, his dog beside him. His cap is a bright red—gay even on a winter's day. His coat is a bright blue, with a golden money-bag hanging at his belt. His breeches are a dark wine red, his stockings a sea-green. On his back he carries a pack.

Some words—worked in by the clever craftsman—tell his story. 'This window, by tradition, represents a benefactor who about the year 1500, left to the church a piece of land later known as Pedlar's Acre, on which the County Hall now stands.' Outlines of two well-known London buildings—the County Hall, standing proudly by the river, and the old Church of St Mary's, where the window of the little Pedlar now is—have also been worked in.

It's an exciting story! Nobody knows now, for sure, when first the little Pedlar's window was put into the church, but we know that it was mended once (in 1608), renewed once (in 1703), and once (in 1884) removed from another part to where it now is. In 1941, during the air-raids on London, a dreadful thing happened—the window got broken, together with a lot of other things in the church. When the news got round, the people were very sad—especially the boys and girls. They couldn't bear to think of the little Pedlar being hurt. And when, in 1956, they heard that he was going to be put back into his place they were delighted.

There he is today, in his cap of bright, bright red, his coat of blue, his breeches of wine red, and his stockings of sea-green. And, of course, his dog is beside him—for he wouldn't be at all happy without his dog.

Long, long ago, the little Pedlar, carrying his pack on

his back, was going through London, not far from St Mary's. But London, in those days, was very different from what it is today—just a small town beside the river. There were a few shops and streets and houses, but many fewer people.

Quite suddenly, the little Pedlar noticed his dog behaving in a strange way. At first, he thought it might be a rabbit that was exciting him. But no rabbit ran out. What could it be? In a moment he saw the cause of the excitement—a box of golden treasure! The little Pedlar couldn't think what to do till he remembered the law of the land, that if anyone found treasure, and he could buy the land where it was found, it was *his* treasure.

So the little Pedlar, with his excited dog beside him, hastily covered over the place where the treasure lay. Then grasping his staff, he hurried off and bought the piece of land. When it was safely his, he returned with his dog and uncovered the golden treasure. In that moment he became a rich man. All the treasure was his! But he didn't for one moment think of keeping it for himself: he gave a generous part of it to the Church. That is why the old Church of St Mary's, Lambeth, remembers him today for his generous heart.

A VISITORS' BOOK

ONE of the nicest things is to go on a visit to friends.

If you came to my house, I should ask you to do something special for me—put your name into my visitors' book. It is a fat cheery red book. Already there are a lot of names in it. The oldest to put his name was an old gentleman of ninety-five; the youngest, a little boy called Ross, who could only make a cross when his father held his little fist.

I don't know when people first started keeping visitors' books; I wish I did. I'm sorry they weren't used much earlier, because in a little village called Bethany you can read about in the New Testament there was a friendly home to which a special Visitor often came. How lovely it would have been if Mary and Martha and brother Lazarus had kept a visitors' book! There was a little home at the end of the Emmaus Road, to which the same Visitor came at the end of a walk with the two people who lived there. After they had sat and talked together, and had eaten a meal, they knew Him for a very special Friend. It would be lovely to have had His signature—perhaps He would have put it in the form of a cross, like little Ross—not because He couldn't write, but because the cross has always been His special mark.

Much nearer our time, I am sorry there was no visitors' book in that little mountain house of Sam Pollard. That was in China. It was such a funny little house. He called it, with a chuckle, his 'little five-pound missionary house'. But it would have needed a big fat visitors' book, for so many friends came there—and one very special Friend, the Friend who long ago came to the house of Mary and Martha and their brother, and to the house of the people at the end of the Emmaus Road.

Sam Pollard was a very friendly man. He travelled all

up and down the mountains to bring love and learning and healing to the Miao people. For a long time he travelled alone. A church was built at a place called Stone Gateway. Then the people began to think how much better it would be for everybody—Sam Pollard especially—if his wife and children could come and live with him. So they built the little house.

It was a funny little house, because there was no level ground on which to put it. So the Miao Christians built it against a mountain—with the mountain for its back wall. It had three other walls—three thin walls—and it had three rooms. The room in the middle was the largest—Sam's living-room by day, and his bedroom by night. What served as his table in the day-time became his bed at night. It sounds rather hard. The fireplace was a large iron pan on a frame; and since it had no chimney, it could be moved. In one corner was a book-store, with stories in Chinese. That was a corner the children specially loved. And on one end of the table, always ready, stood medicine bottles and jars of vaseline and boracic-acid—for Sam Pollard was doctor, as well as missionary-teacher.

Next was a tiny room with a looking-glass and wash-basin and a brush-and-comb and towel. There wasn't much space. Sometimes the wash-basin had also to act as till, and hold the cash from the sale of books.

The third little room had cups and plates and knives and chop-sticks, and flour and sugar and potatoes.

It was all a great squeeze, but nobody minded. Besides the grown-ups, the children were always running in and out of that little house. 'Try as you would,' said Sam, 'you could not get angry with them; and as to chasing them away, they just gloried in that. One could not help loving the children. I was always glad to see them in the little five-pound missionary house. . . .

'Wonderful little five-pound house! Wonderful little rooms. Bed-room and dining-room, dispensary and book room, and preachers' training classroom—yes, and it was one thing more . . . Jesus was with us. He sat at table and broke bread with us, it was He Who came in the person of all those sick ones and all those troubled ones.'

If only Sam Pollard had kept a visitors' book in that funny little house! And yet—as in my house—the best Name wouldn't be there, because in a way, He really isn't a visitor at all; He lives there all the time (Matthew 28[20]).

AT THE ZOO

I LOVE a day at a zoo; don't you? It's such fun to see the peacocks, with their tails shimmering in the sun, and the giraffes, with their funny long necks, and their heads among the tree-tops. But best of all—if one can get a pocketful of pea-nuts—are the cages where the monkeys live. They are such funny fellows.

In one zoo, there once lived a nice old Mrs Monkey. One day somebody gave her a little piece of looking-glass. Then she managed somehow to get hold of a big piece of newspaper. Crushing it up, she perched it on to her head —and there she sat, holding her little piece of looking-glass in one hand, and using the other hand to tuck in her newspaper hat, with a touch here and a touch there.

In another zoo there was an old Mr Monkey—a very solemn old Mr Monkey. One week the painters had been at the zoo, painting all the insides of the cages, making them sweet and clean. And Mr Monkey got himself from somewhere a little piece of rope which he held tightly in his little fist and made bristly at the end. Then he sat and very solemnly swept it up and down with fine strokes, and from side to side.

Now you mustn't be offended if I suggest that boys and girls are just a little bit like monkeys. I will tell you what I mean. Once, in a little town where I lived, there was a little boy called Laurie John. His Daddy had a shop in the main street. Laurie John had a head of golden curly hair and wasn't quite five.

Every Saturday night, the Salvation Army Band used to come down the street and stand in front of his Daddy's shop. They wore their uniforms, with the fine caps and bonnets, and they carried their great instruments, shining bright, that made a great deal of music all at once. They stood in a ring, and played and sang, and prayed, and told wonderful stories, and took up a collection. And Laurie John noticed this week after week.

Then his birthday came near and he said to his Daddy one morning at breakfast: 'I'm going to be five tomorrow. What are you going to give me for my birthday?'

His Daddy said: 'Is it really tomorrow? Now what do you want?'

'Do you know what I want more than anything else in the whole world?' asked Laurie John. 'An Army Band!'

Well, his Daddy thought that was really a rather big order for one little boy, just five. But because he was a nice Daddy, he went down the street, and in a shop he found a beautiful trumpet—with a cord on it, and a very nice note. He brought it home, and Laurie John was delighted.

Next Saturday night, after tea, I went down the street to post a letter, and I saw the Salvation Army come up the street as usual. I saw them stand in a great ring, and I saw over on the other side, somebody just five years old, with golden curly hair. And when the big bandsman took up his shining instrument and drew breath to play, that somebody, just five years old, took up his, and puffed out his cheeks to play. And I saw that when the big bandsman took his instrument, and set it down on the gravel, to pray, that somebody just five years old, with golden curly hair, took his music and put it down on the gravel, and closed his eyes to pray.

Now it is fair, isn't it, to say that boys and girls are just *a little bit* like monkeys. We all copy. That is the wonderful way God has made us. So that it is very exciting to have story-books, and read of fine heroes and heroines who do things. We can copy them—and we do it almost without thinking. That is the best part of having fine fathers and mothers, and aunts and uncles, and teachers— we can copy them. Of course, we don't always know we're doing it.

That is what happened to the friends of Jesus long ago;

they loved Him, and followed Him—and without thinking about it, they copied Him. And people said: 'These men have been with Jesus!' ('They took knowledge of them, that they had been with Jesus', Acts 4[13]). Now how could they tell? Oh, easy! Something of His great courage showed in their courage; and something of His kindness, in their kindness; and the way they helped people was a copy of the way He did it. It was a wonderful thing to happen!

Wouldn't it be lovely if it happened here—to you, and your friends? And it could, you know—if you love Him, and learn about Him, and talk to Him in prayer, and follow Him every day as your Greatest Friend. Something of His courage will become your courage, and something of His kindness, and His joy, and His love. For God has made you that way—to copy. I can't think of anything more wonderful.

WHEN MARKO CAME HOME

MARKO had never been far from home. Like his father and grandfather before him, he had been born in the beautiful little country of Serbia. He lived a simple life, as all the peasants did, rising early when the sun came over the rim of the hills. He had a fine, strong body, so that when the sun set, and the old people were ready to rest, Marko and his young friends sang their national songs and danced. Sometimes they told ancient stories that had been handed down.

Then, sad to say, everything was changed; war came, and war always changes things. Marko was called from his happy life, to do orderly work. Nine of his friends shared it with him. It was not very exciting work for young, strong men. They had to keep the soldiers' mess-room clean and tidy, get the officers' meals, and help keep the equipment in order. Every day when they arose, the same round of tasks awaited them, and they found it dull.

Soon, word came to the General that the ten young orderlies had become careless in their work. The General knew that he would have to do something about it, so he called them before him. When they stood before him—more than a little ashamed—the General, to their great surprise, began with the word 'brothers'. 'Brothers,' said he, quietly and simply, 'you are here to render service to myself and my officers. Let your service be done joyously and perfectly. That is all.' Hardly able to believe their ears, Marko and his friends went back to their tasks and for a while things improved.

But news came again to the ear of the General. Sorrowfully he turned it over in his mind. Then he knew what he would do. That night, as the young men were settling for sleep, the flap of their tent was raised, and their General himself appeared. 'Good-night, brothers,' said he, 'I hope all is well with you.' And with that he was gone.

Marko and his comrades managed a gruff 'Good-night!' But when the tent-flap was down again, and they were sure they were alone, they spoke their minds freely. 'Brothers?' they said. 'Who is he calling "brothers"? Don't we do all the work?' And in that grumbling mood they fell asleep.

In the morning, to their astonishment, when they opened their eyes, they saw just inside the tent, the officers' boots, all beautifully polished, set out in a row. To do the boots was part of their task, and when they saw them done they could hardly believe their eyes. 'Surely,' they said, 'one of the old Serbian stories has come alive— whilst we have slept, the elves have come down from the woods, and done our task for us.' More astonished were they when they crossed over to where the officers met, and found the fire burning merrily and the place swept.

All that day they talked among themselves in whispers, hardly daring to speak to the others of the strange happenings.

That night, they went again to their tent to sleep. When they awakened, astonishment was piled on astonishment, for they found that the same thing had happened again—the officers' boots, all beautifully polished, stood in a neat row just inside the tent.

That night, only nine young men slept, and one kept watch. For a long time no sound disturbed the deep snoring of the nine. Nobody stirred. Then a little before dawn, the boots, beautifully polished, appeared once more in a row just inside the tent. The young watchman wakened his comrades. 'It's the General!' he cried. 'The General!' Marko and the others sat up, and rubbed their sleepy eyes. 'The General?' they queried. 'The General?' Now they were really puzzled. But soon Marko, as leader, was called before the General. As he stood, not sure what

D

would happen, the foolish talk of two nights earlier passed before his mind.

'Marko,' began the General, 'did you ever hear of Jesus Christ?'

'Yes, sir,' said Marko, a little taken aback.

'Then,' his General went on quietly, 'you may remember that once in an Upper Room, He laid aside His garments, and with water in a servant's basin, and a towel, He stooped to wash His disciples' feet. They were quarrelsome, thinking only who would be greatest. "He who would be greatest", said He, "must be servant of all." '

Marko's head hung in silence, as the words sought out the deep places of his heart.

'Marko,' added the quiet voice, 'I am your General, but I have shown you that I can do your work. And you must not think I have not enjoyed doing it'—and as Marko found courage to look up, he saw his General's eyes. 'In every perfect service,' he added, 'there is hidden a great treasure. Whoever serves—freely and joyously— he finds God! Remember the Master's words in the Upper Room: "If ye know these things, *happy are ye if ye do them*." '

When the glad day came at last that war was at an end, Marko and his comrades came back home. But it wasn't long before those who knew them best, knew that they had a new Marko in their midst. He sought now only to fill his life with loving thought of others. And that was how, in time, he came to get his wonderful nick-name: they called him: 'The Man of Perfect Service.'

THE COMICAL BLIND MAN

ONE early morning in the city of Christchurch the sun shone on the shops and the houses and gardens, and on the trees lining the banks of the river. Everything seemed as usual—cars and vans hurrying along—till presently I came to a street where some of them were parked. And there I saw a sight so strange that I couldn't believe it.

Parked at the kerb-side was a van with words painted in large red letters across its back: CAUTION—BLIND MAN DRIVING!

I read the large red letters again: CAUTION—BLIND MAN DRIVING! How could a blind man be allowed to drive? Surely there would be accidents. My eyes moved with curiosity all over that van. Next, I found some lettering on the back of it—not quite so large as on the side. Suddenly I began to chuckle—it was a tradesman's van, and this was his comical way of advertising that he had a certain make of venetian blind for sale. Day after day he went about his business in the city with those words showing on his van: BLIND MAN DRIVING. He had certainly caught me out beautifully, and got my attention in exactly the way he had hoped he might.

There are, of course, several sorts of blind men. Can you think of some of them? First of all, there is the man who sells blinds. Then there is the blind man who cannot see, and must find his way about as best he can, with the aid of a white stick. And then, more surprising, there is the man who, although he has eyes, cannot, or will not, see. Helen Keller, blind, deaf and dumb since she was a little girl, now one of the most wonderful women, and honoured the world over, says that that is the worst kind of blindness of all. She says: 'I know many people who have perfect eyes, but are really blind. Their eyes are open, but their hearts are closed.'

I wonder if you know anybody like that? *You* wouldn't be blind like that, would you? It's a very sad kind of blindness, and more deserving of pity, Helen Keller thinks, than her own blindness. Because whatever people's eyes are like when their hearts are closed, it is very hard for beautiful things to get into their lives.

That's what Jesus found when He went about day after day in Palestine with His twelve disciples. For a time they argued among themselves, about who should be greatest. Then Jesus knew that beautiful thoughts weren't getting in. So He said to them this surprising thing, that is now set down in our New Testament: 'You have eyes, do you not see?' (Mark 8[18], Moffatt).

So the little prayer that somebody wrote, needs often to be on your lips and mine:

> *Thou Who hast given me eyes to see*
> *And love this sight so fair,*
> *Give me a heart to find out Thee,*
> *And read Thee everywhere.*

THE ROYAL BANQUET

IT was a happy day for the Spanish people of the beautiful city of Madrid. At long last, the palace that had taken twenty-six years to build, was finished. When the old wooden palace had been burned down, the people said there would never be such a palace again, but now the new palace had arisen, great and grand.

Some of the old treasures had been lost in the fire, but soon they brought new ones. The ceilings were high, and from a vaulted hall rose a grand stair-case. All the servants wore the royal livery—and very grand they looked, in their blue tail-coats, fastened with brass buttons.

Many a boy in Madrid fell off to sleep at night dreaming that a day might come when he would be called to serve their good King, Alfonso the Twelfth. Strange to say, some of the boys, once installed in the palace, grew careless, and one day news came to the ears of the King himself that some of them even neglected to say their grace before meals. The King was very troubled about this, and for a while he was puzzled what to do. Then suddenly, a fine plan came to him.

'I will give a splendid banquet,' he said, 'and all my servant boys shall be invited to it. They will like that. And I will dine with them myself. They will like that, too.'

In the great hall the banquet was set. It was a wonderful banquet; on the table were all the things that boys love, and the King sat at the head.

But when the meal was ready, the boys, seeing the good things before them, started at once to eat, as the King feared they would.

But the King had already worked out only part of his plan, and half-way through the meal he arranged for a poor, ill-clad beggar to push in and seat himself at the royal table. When the boy-servants, looking up a moment, saw him come in, they were horrified, and they expected King Alfonso to order him out. But strange as it seemed to them, he didn't. At last, when the beggar had eaten well, he rose from the table, and without so much as a word of thanks, left. That was too much for the boy-servants—they could keep quiet no longer. One by one, each rose and spoke about the beggar's rudeness and ingratitude, calling him all sorts of names. They could hardly think of names bad enough for him.

But as the last spoke, suddenly, to their surprise, their King himself rose, and never as long as they lived would they forget his words: 'Boys, bolder than this beggar have you all been. Every day you sit down to a table supplied by your Heavenly Father; yet you ask not His blessing, nor express to Him your thanks.'

And all up and down the table, the boy-servants who listened to the words of their King hung their heads. But never again did they sit down to a meal without remembering to say their thanks to Him who gave it, God their Heavenly King.

WILLIE, FULL OF MISCHIEF

THERE never was a jollier family than the Jacksons, nor one so full of mischief, and Willie was the leader of them all. There were five children when Willie was born, and by and by there were three more.

Visitors to their London home were horrified to see Willie sliding down the glass roof of the conservatory, or hanging on to a chimney-pot on the roof of the cottage in the garden and proclaiming himself 'King of the Castle!' Occasionally they found him tearing round on his bicycle, ducking his head at the right moment when he came to the low doorway into the stable-yard. They held their breath when they saw the things he did, and they were more astonished when they learned that he was blind!

One of Willie's joys, when he was not pulling his bicycle to bits and putting it together again, was to waken early and go out. The only bother was to get his young brother to go with him. An alarm-clock was not allowed, but Willie invented a fine contraption of string, weights and pulleys and fish-hooks, that worked from an alarm-clock at a distance. At precisely five o'clock it lifted the bed-clothes off his young brother, whether he wanted to get up or not.

Willie was eleven before he went to school, though already he had been doing lessons for some time—first, with an elderly gentleman, himself blind. But his young pupil was so quick, that in no time he was ready for more advanced braille, and another teacher had to be found. Willie could easily read the raised dots on the thick page of his book. He had a special board for doing sums, his memory was good, and he learned music, too, so that by the time he was eleven he was really doing all the usual things—swimming, rowing, gym, gardening, and 'conker fights'. He was also very good at midnight feasts in the dormitory.

But he had his serious thoughts. By the time he had got his matric, and had been confirmed at a beautiful service in the church, he was thinking of what he wanted to do in the world. Some thought he should be a lawyer like his father, but Willie's mind was already made up, and he never changed it.

His brothers and sisters would have helped him with his packing, when the time came to go up to the great university, but he hated fuss. So he packed up his own things, and moved himself to Oxford. Soon he had many new friends. One of his early misadventures befell when he invited three of them to tea. Somehow, by accident, he poured the milk into the sugar-basin.

There were then very few books in braille for blind students. Willie had to hire a reader to read to him out of ordinary books, and that made everything much harder. But Willie got on splendidly, and by the end of three years of solid hard work he found that he had won honours in his two most important subjects.

From Oxford, Willie Jackson went on to a special college for young men who wanted to be ministers, and when he was twenty-three he was ordained to be a minister.

He was sent, at first, to a big church not far from London, where there were lots of boys. They soon made friends. They called him Father Jackson. The boys were terribly proud of the things he could do—dive off the deep end of the swimming-pool, ride his bicycle at speed through the streets when they all set off together, make up amusing songs and set them to his own tunes. And that wasn't half the things they shared—for in church, and when they gathered in his rooms, or set off on outings together, he told them wonderful stories about the Best Master a boy can have.

At the end of four happy years, when news reached the

boys that Father Jackson was to go to another church, they were broken-hearted. But the next church was in a very poor slum part of London. Father Jackson soon had another bunch of boys round him. And they were just as broken-hearted when time came for him to leave them.

This time he was being called to the work to which he gave all the rest of his life. Again, it was with boys. It was in Burma—a hot country, about which many people didn't know very much, save that there were a lot of blind boys there. A little school had been started for them, at a place called Kemendine.

When blind Father Jackson knew that they wanted him, he didn't hesitate for a moment. All his prayers were full of thanksgiving to God for giving him the chance.

By the time he had been on the boat a week or so, he had already learned a hundred and fifty words in Burmese, the curly-lettered language of the boys to whom he was going. He was so keen.

There were eighty blind boys at the little school, and they gave Father Jackson a wonderful welcome. They felt, in a special way, that he was their friend, because he was blind too. And soon they called him by a special name—*Apay-gyi*—'Big Father'. Soon they were just as proud of the things he could do as the other boys had been. But now he did things he had never done before; he put off his English clothes and put on Burmese ones so that he would be like his boys. He slept on the floor just as they did; in the daytime, he shared in all the work— cooking the rice, washing the clothes, scrubbing to keep everything healthy and clean. More than that, he invented a way of writing Burmese words specially for blind boys, and made a printing-press for them. The only way he knew to make it was to hammer out letters from flattened kerosene-tins and with the help of the boys put them through an old mangle.

He taught his boys to make cane baskets, and toys, and mats, to do carpentry, and to make chairs and mend

E

shoes. He taught them songs and plays, and he took some of them long journeys into the jungle to hunt for other boys who were blind. They were hard, adventurous journeys—sometimes on foot, sometimes in lumbering bullock-carts. People said: 'How can a blind man make such journeys? A blind man can't see snakes, or other wild creatures; a blind man can't cross a rickety bridge made of a single bamboo.' But somehow, blind Father Jackson, the 'Big Father' of Kemendine, did all these things. And every day, wherever they were, he told them of God, the Great Father, and of His close everlasting love—*and because they loved their earthly friend, they learned to love God, of whom he told.*

A LITTLE GIRL WITH A HOOP

IT was a joyous day for the Mumford family and their friends when the little new baby was born. From the first, she was not very strong, and her mother had to keep her snuggled up close and warm. They called her Catherine. No one guessed then that a day would come when her name would be loved all round the world.

It all began a few years later, when she was playing with her hoop, bowling it along in the sun, in fine style. One moment the street was clear, next, round the corner came two men followed by a jeering crowd of men and boys. Surprised, little Catherine stopped, and held her hoop close. Another little girl might have run home quickly to her mother, but not Catherine. She wanted to see what would happen.

The jeering crowd broke up as a big policeman appeared and arrested one of them. Little Catherine couldn't tell what he had done, but he looked poor and shabby and friendless. And at once, she was standing not only *on* his side but *by* his side. The policeman led off his prisoner, and little Catherine, carrying her hoop, marched with him all the way to the police-station.

Catherine never forgot that day—her first march!

When she reached her early twenties, she fell in love with a young man named William. He was a young preacher—a very unusual one. As long as he could remember, he had had a great struggle; his father had died, and he had been put to work in a pawnbroker's shop.

But William loved God with all his young heart, and he determined to learn all he could and to do something good in the world. He moved to London, to work in another pawnbroker's shop, and nearly starved himself to send part of his small wages to his mother and sisters.

The pawnbroker's shop stood in a very poor part of the

city, and William was surrounded every day by poor people. He learned about their struggles to get work, to buy food, to clothe their children. Many knew no other way to forget their struggles but to get drunk—and that only made things worse.

On Sunday, William used to preach in the little chapel at Brixton. There he met Catherine. She was still not very robust, but her spirit was as strong and full of life as the young preacher's. Together they began to plan what they would do in the world. William had had little schooling, but Catherine helped him all she could. When he was away on his preaching journeys he used to send back to her parcels of his clothes to darn and patch.

They got married. So Catherine was able to share in everything that William planned. They began a new kind of army—with uniforms and flags. But it was an army without guns—The Salvation Army. It was Catherine's suggestion that they should start in London, and on a piece of ground in Whitechapel pitch a tent. Day by day, and night by night, in that desperately poor part of London, they did wonderful things. They gathered about them other young men and women who loved God with all their hearts—and the poor as well. They had open-air meetings, they marched, they rallied people with their drums and songs. Nothing like it had ever happened before. At first, lots of people didn't understand; they even threw things at them—rotten eggs and squashy vegetables. It took a lot of courage. But little by little the police, as well as the poor people, came to see that the officers of the Salvation Army were their best friends.

And the Army that Catherine and William started grew and grew till it reached right round the world.

When at last Catherine died, she had millions of friends who thanked God that once a little girl stopped bowling her hoop in the sun to march with a poor prisoner. And William, her husband—General William Booth by this time—said a wonderful thing about her: '*She was a thorough hater*,' he said, '*she was love*.' He knew where she'd got that secret—she had found the place in the Bible where it says: 'Ye that *love* the Lord, *hate* evil' (Psalm 97[10]). And all her life she loved God; all her life she hated evil. That was her secret, and she needed no other.

WITH THE RED INDIANS

THE young white man's eyes danced with eagerness. Egerton Young knew full well that there would be great lakes to cross and trails in the forest where it would be hard to find the way. But he was ready. He knew there would be rushing rivers, with swirling rapids where no boat could live. Then, like the Red Indians, who carried their beautiful canoes of birch-bark, he meant to travel on foot. He was ready to pitch his tent on the sandy river-beaches, or sleep on the hard rocks under the stars; he was ready to hunt for animals in the forest, to get his food. The trail might be hard to find, and he might get lost, but he was ready to try. 'If the Indians can travel the trail to "the land of the North Wind",' said he, 'so can I.' He wanted to follow them as they went hunting and trapping, and if possible make friends. In his pack he carried a few bottles of medicines—and a book with the greatest story in the world.

Usually the Indian braves were ready to listen to the stranger with the pale face as they gathered in their encampments. Sometimes they came out of curiosity to see what he was like; sometimes to hear the strange things he had to say. Most were friendly.

Once, as he told them part of the story in his great Book, he wished he could set up school and teach them to read and write. But Egerton Young could carry no more than his own papers and pencils, and no supply of books to go round. Near by stood a great grey rock as high as a house in the country he had come from. One side was smooth as a blackboard. It made a fine place on which to write. Suddenly he realized he had no chalk, but next minute his eyes spotted at his feet burnt sticks from the camp fire. He picked up the one that lay nearest and wrote up one single word of six letters: MANETO. At once an excited cry arose, for it was their word for God, for the Great Spirit, as they called Him.

Little by little, each time the young missionary met them, he told them more. There was so much to tell. And always on the trail he kept coming across Indians he had not met before.

Once, in the deep woods, he came upon three hundred chiefs and braves. They were sitting in a silent ring—a sight never to be forgotten. Egerton Young stepped into their midst. When he had finished telling part of the great story he had come to tell, one chief after another rose to ask him questions. The last to speak was an old man, with a long plait of hair showing from under his head-dress, and a look of excitement in his eyes.

'Missionary,' he began, 'once my hair was black like the crow's wings; now it is white. Grey hairs on my head, and grand-children in the wigwam, tell me that I have not long to live. Yet I never heard such things as you have told today. They were very sweet to my ears. Missionary, you called the Great Spirit "Father".'

'Yes,' replied Egerton Young, 'I did. I taught you to begin the great Prayer, "Our Father, which art in heaven, Hallowed be Thy name".'

'That is new, and very sweet to our ears,' said the old Indian. ' We never thought to call Him by that name. We have heard His power in the thunder, and seen His might in the lightning, in the tempest, and in the blizzard —and we have been afraid. So that what you tell us is very sweet to us.' Then, pausing a moment, he went on: 'And, missionary, did you say that the Great Spirit is your Father, too?'

'Yes,' said Egerton Young, eagerly, '*your Father—and my Father.*'

The old man repeated it: 'The Indian's Father—and the white man's Father? *Then we are brothers!*'

At that, a cry of joy rose from those round the camp fire in the forest. And no wonder, for they had discovered one of the most wonderful things in the whole world: *that God is our Father, and all men everywhere are our brothers!*

FOOLISH CROCODILES

ALL over the world there are people who love flowers; all over the world there are people who love animals. But Mr Richard St Barbe Baker is different from these—above everything, he loves trees. He loves to plant them, care for them, look at them, and study them. And he has founded a Society called The Men of the Trees, that now reaches right round the world to link those who love trees.

Mr St Barbe Baker has written books about the adventures that have befallen him as he has travelled about the world.

In one of them, *Africa Drums*, he tells of a strange adventure. He was travelling in that great country, far from towns, where the only places to sleep at night were little bush huts called 'rest houses'. They were comfortable, in a way, but all about them were stinging and biting insects. Tsetse flies, and gigas, and scorpions were horrible things, but mosquitoes with their sharp little stings were the worst, because they could give travellers malaria.

In that part of the great country of Africa, there were also crocodiles—and they gave Mr St Barbe Baker his strangest adventure.

'One day,' he said, 'I was trekking in the Ogba reserve, not far from Benin, a new part of the forest. I cut my way into a little clearing where there was a small village.

' "Who lives here?" I asked my interpreter, Igabon. "What is this village?"

'This is the village of "the crocodile-catchers",' he replied.

' "The crocodile-catchers?"

' "Yes," he said, "the crocodile-catchers." '

Then Mr St Barbe Baker and Igabon went on further till they came to a ju-ju shrine.

'That,' he explained—'was the ju-ju of these crocodile-catchers; in other words, it was where they made their prayers for good luck and no harm. . . . At the shrine I saw the son of one of them; farther on I met a very old man whose skin seemed to hang like scales, more like the skin of a crocodile than of a human. Igabon told me that this was the chief crocodile-catcher himself. After greeting him, I asked: "Is it true that you catch crocodiles?" '

'He said, "Yes", so I said: "Isn't that very dangerous?" The old man laughed, and answered: "Crocodiles be fools. They're very easy to catch."

' "Do tell me, how do you do it?"

'And then he explained how they waited till the river was low in the dry season, then dug a deep narrow trench leading out of the river. At the end of the trench he made a cage into which he put a living goat. The crocodile tried to get the goat, but he could not, because it was in the cage. So he tried to turn round and come back, but he could not, because the trench was too narrow. Then he tried to climb the walls, but they were too steep. The old man laughed as he said: "Crocodiles . . . they are not fit to walk back. And so we come and tie their heads to their tails with ropes. Then we carry them to Benin, where they are sacrificed." '

So Mr St Barbe Baker learnt the art of crocodile catching.

Wide-awake boys and girls would have more sense than crocodiles—foolish crocodiles. You wouldn't let anyone in the playground, or in the street, lead you into a place, or a plan, where it wasn't easy to turn back, would you?

But in the Bible there is a warning, just in case you should forget. It says: *Take heed that thou be not snared* (Deuteronomy 12^{30}).

THE STOVE-PIPE HAT

IT seemed to little Charlie McLean that the great day would never come. He found it the hardest thing in the world to wait.

It was going to be a great honour for the town of Philadelphia to have Mr Lincoln stop there on his way to Washington to be made President. Charlie's father— Mr George McLean—was helping to arrange the little ceremony in Philadelphia, and he hoped with all his heart that everything would go without a hitch.

Already a big wooden platform was up. To little Charlie it looked huge, more than big enough to hold a seat for the great man and the important people who would want to be present to see the flag hoisted over Independence Hall.

'Whereabouts shall we sit?' asked Charlie. For his father had promised that he would squeeze him in beside himself up on the platform.

'Wait and see!' said Mr McLean. 'Have no fear, you'll be close enough to see and to hear the great man.'

'What if he speaks to me?' said Charlie. 'What shall I say?'

'You chatter too much,' said his father, 'away off to bed with you, or you won't be ready.'

Charlie seemed hardly to have dropped off to sleep when it was time to waken and get dressed.

At the expected time the great man arrived. Everything, Charlie's father was glad to think, was going according to plan. Mr Lincoln had taken his seat on the platform, surrounded by the important people. Down below the platform, packed close, were many others. At the proper time, Mr Lincoln rose, and taking off his tall, black, stove-pipe hat, laid it down on the flat railing at the platform's edge. His mind was already on what he was going to say to the people gathered before him, all eager for his words.

But it was a grown-up's speech; and the eyes of one little boy began to move from the speaker's face. Next moment Charlie's eyes fell on that tall stove-pipe hat. His hands itched to reach out and touch it—find out what it felt like. It was too big a temptation.

Next minute, Charlie had popped it on his own head— just to *feel* what it was like. But it was much bigger and deeper than it looked, and to his surprise, it slipped down right over his forehead, and over his eyes, till its rim rested on his shoulders. And he let out a sudden little gasp.

At that, his father looked round, and was horrified at what he saw. Up till that moment everything had gone according to plan, but whatever would the great man think of this?

'Charlie,' he whispered, giving him a nudge that he hoped none of the important people would see, 'put back Mr Lincoln's hat!'

I do not know whether any of the important people saw what happened or whether the great man, making his speech, ever knew. But when it was all over, Mr Lincoln happened to notice one small boy on the platform, squeezed in between the important people. Someone said his name was Charlie. Next minute, Mr Lincoln's strong, big friendly hand was resting on Charlie's head. 'God bless you, Charlie,' said the great man, 'may you grow up to be a noble, good man.'

The little ceremony of the flag-raising at an end, Mr Lincoln—wearing his tall, black stove-pipe hat—went on his way. The people scattered to their homes. They had heard the speech and seen the flag raised. But nobody guessed that to one small boy something far more important had happened—the great man had asked the special blessing of God on him.

Years later, when he was grown up, Charlie—Charles Clothier McLean—became a minister. And one day—

forty years on—when he was at Douglas Memorial Methodist Church in Washington, D.C., he chanced on a collection of old lantern-slides. And there—to his great happiness and surprise—was one made to record that great day. The person who had taken the photograph, and made the slide, had long forgotten all about it. But there still to be seen—as plain as plain—was the great Mr Lincoln among all the important people on the platform—and there was one small boy—and there was the stove-pipe hat!

Now you may never get the chance to wear a great man's hat—but you *can* wear a great man's courage, a great man's kindness of heart, a great man's love of people!

And if you can do that—*why, you'll be a great man yourself!*

UP THE MOUNTAIN AND DOWN

LITTLE Charles New was born in a Fulham home on a winter's day. He got a great welcome. But nobody, for one moment, thought of Kilimanjaro, the highest mountain in Africa, pushing its great snowy peak up into the sky. Yet now it is impossible to think of Charles New without thinking of Kilimanjaro, or Kilimanjaro without thinking of Charles New. For Charles New was the first European ever to get to the top of that great mountain.

For a long time after he got to Africa, Charles New looked at that great mountain, and one August day, when he was twenty-seven, he knew he could wait no longer. He gathered eleven African boys to go with him, strong and fit, and ready to help with the camping and climbing gear.

The first part of the climb was easy—up the gentle cultivated slopes where round African huts sat squat on the ground, in little villages, and coffee was grown. But soon it got harder.

Up and up they climbed, the wide lands stretching out below them, as far as the eye could see, and still their exploit was little more than begun.

In time, they struck trouble. It wasn't the steepness of the mountain or that an accident befell them. Their first trouble was because of a *mystery*. Long before ever the little party of climbers got as far as the snows, they had to go up over a very rocky part, and one of the native boys suddenly took fright. He was afraid of a mystery—the mystery of echoing voices that came back from the rocky ridges as they talked together. He had never heard echoes before, and he was terrified. He felt sure they were the threats of evil spirits who lived on the mountain, warning them not to climb any further. Exhausted, the other boys soon caught his fear, and at a critical stage ten of them refused to go one step further.

But one boy, Tofiki, wasn't afraid of the mystery voices, and he stayed with Charles New. Tofiki and Charles New pressed on. It was very difficult; they had more to carry, and the way up the mountain was getting steeper all the time. But at last, tired, but happy, they got above the mystery voices, above the dangerous rocky ridges. It was a great joy to them. All around them at the top, the snow was as hard as the rocks over which they had climbed. Charles New managed to crack off a few large pieces with his spiked climbing staff.

When Tofiki saw for the first time in his life, the strange white stones, he was delighted. His plan was to wrap them up in his blanket, and carry them down in triumph to his friends, to prove that he'd really reached the top of the great Kilimanjaro.

At last, when Charles New and Tofiki got down again, Tofiki unrolled his blanket, and showed what remained of the strange white rocks. His friends were open-eyed with wonder. When Charles took up some of the smaller pieces, and put them between his teeth, they cried: 'Whoever saw man eating stones before?' Others planned to sell the 'white stuff' from the mountains, for medicine. 'It will melt before you can do that,' said Charles. But they only laughed, 'Whoever heard of stones melting?'

Charles New[1] never looked at that great mountain after that, as he went about his work among the African people below, but he thought of those two strange happenings—the mystery of the echo, and the foolish talk about the white stones. During those happy, crowded years, he taught them things more important by far than the secret of the mystery voices and the knowledge of the

[1] Today, boys and girls who worship in Walham Grove Methodist Church, Fulham, see a plaque on the wall, bearing his name. It says that he was 'For ten years a missionary of the United Methodist Free Churches in Eastern Africa', and that 'he died . . . in an attempt to carry the Gospel into the interior . . . at the early age of thirty-five'.

snow: he taught them the meaning of Love. For there was a verse in his New Testament which he could never forget, which said: 'Though I understand all *mysteries*, and *all knowledge* . . . and have not Love, I am nothing' (1 Corinthians 13^2). And that was worth going all the way to Africa to teach.